BRUNEL
ROYAL ALBERT BRIDGE

by A.R. Kingdom

**ARK PUBLICATIONS
(RAILWAYS)**

First published in 2006 by ARK PUBLICATIONS (RAILWAYS), an imprint of FOREST PUBLISHING, Woodstock, Liverton, Newton Abbot, Devon TQ12 6JJ

British Library Cataloguing in Publication Data
A catalogue record for this book is available from the British Library
ISBN 1–873029–13–6

The Royal Albert Bridge on 2nd May 1959, exactly 100 years after its opening, showing ex-GWR 2-6-0 No. 6301 running into Saltash whilst on the 5.30 a.m. service from Paddington to Penzance.

Peter W. Gray

ARK PUBLICATIONS (RAILWAYS)
Editorial, layout and design by:
Mike Lang

Typeset by:
Carnaby Typesetting, Torquay, Devon TQ1 1EG

Printed and bound in Great Britain by:
Wotton Printers Limited, Newton Abbot, Devon TQ12 4PJ

Cover photographs:

Front – An evening view of the Royal Albert Bridge in the year of its centenary when, for this one summer only, it was floodlit each night.

Peter W. Gray

Back – A distant view of the bridge clearly showing the modern extra strengthening stays against the darkened background of the road bridge deck, 16th April 2003.

John Gilpin

CONTENTS

Page

ACKNOWLEDGEMENTS

The author is indebted to the following in the production of this book.

Mr Brendan Hanrahan, editor of the *Herald Express,* for permission to quote from various 'Rail Trail' articles written by Mr Peter Gray and which have appeared in his newspaper on a weekly basis since 1985.

Wood & Tozer, former printers and publishers of Devonport.

Larry Crosier; Stephen Fuller; Bryan Gibson; John Gilpin; Peter Gray; Mike Lang; Bernard Mills.

(Photographs are acknowledged individually in most instances.)

DEDICATION

No. 5 in this popular series is dedicated to the greatest engineer of them all, Isambard Kingdom Brunel. It has been published to commemorate the bi-centenary of his birth on 9th April 1806 and focuses on one of his greatest achievements – the Royal Albert Bridge at Saltash, connecting Cornwall to Devon by rail.

A. R. Kingdom

INTRODUCTION

As 2006 dawned, the pace to commemorate the birth of Brunel quickened nationally and particularly so here in the West Country.

I have had in my possession for many years a little booklet entitled *History of the Royal Albert Bridge...,* which was printed and published by Wood & Tozer of Devonport and whose contents form the main basis of this book. Produced shortly after the opening ceremony, its description of the building of the Saltash Bridge – as it is known locally – is detailed, accurate and colourful, commensurate with the language in use at the time. Therefore, I make no apology for reproducing its contents verbatim, especially as modern English often falls short of the 19th century standard of reporting.

To supplement it, a short postscript follows indicating salient points in the bridge's history since that momentous occasion on 2nd May 1859. In addition, I have been able to include from my photographic collection four original and hitherto unpublished studies of the bridge taken in 1892, following the changeover from broad- to standard-gauge track in May of that year. These were the work of J. B. N. Ashford, a locomotive inspector for the GWR and who was very active with his camera for many years from around the latter part of the 19th century. Three of these photographs show close-ups of the interior of the spans before the new ballast and track work were sullied and tarnished by the constant passing of trains.

One evening, whilst discussing the imminent publication of *Tavistock North & South* (No. 4 in this series), I casually mentioned to my publisher, Mike Lang, the afore-going facts. "Well, go for it then, but we must try to produce it within a month or so or we will miss the boat," was his surprising reply! This meant the end of my spring break and the start of a frenzied search through my photographic collection and files, plus the calling on my railway friends for urgent favours.

I can now only hope the fruits of our joint efforts bear sufficient tribute to the great man and his masterpiece across the River Tamar.

A.R. Kingdom

April 2006

A photograph of the Royal Albert Bridge taken from the road bridge between St Budeaux (Plymouth) and Saltash, as 4–6–0 No. 7022 *Hereford Castle* brings the relief to the 4.50 p.m. from Penzance to Manchester across in subdued evening light on 4th August 1962.

Peter W. Gray

HISTORY

OF THE

Royal Albert Bridge

FOR THE CORNWALL RAILWAY,

ACROSS THE RIVER TAMAR,

AT

SALTASH.

WITH ILLUSTRATIONS.

Engineer—I. K. BRUNEL, Esq.

Contractors—Messrs. HUDSON & MALE.

Printed and Published by

WOOD & TOZER, 39, Fore Street, Devonport.

Sold by all Booksellers and at the Railway Book-stalls.

PRICE ONE PENNY.

Royal Albert Bridge, Saltash.

The "Royal Albert Bridge," across the River Tamar at Saltash, represents a wrought-iron structure, 2,200 feet, or nearly half-a-mile in length; the span of each of the openings from the centre of one pier to the centre of the other, being 455 feet; the height of the centre pier from the foundation in the bed of the river 240 feet; height of roadway above high water mark, 110 feet. The main openings are spanned by oval tubes, whose diameters are 17 feet by 12 feet, the ends of which are connected by chains, together forming a parabolic curve, and from these chains is suspended the roadway. To prevent the sacking down of the tube, at intervals of forty feet occur vertical strutts above the points of suspension, diagonal braces connecting the strutts for the purpose of distributing the load, the weight of the section over each opening being 1,100 tons. These sections stand with their shore ends on brick pillars, surmounting granite and lime-stone piers, and their other ends on standards supported by four hollow octagonal cast iron columns, 10 feet in diameter, and resting on a solid granite circular pier 35 feet in diameter, built in the centre of the river, and standing 12 feet above high water mark – two of the iron columns supporting each section. From the bottom of the roadway to the top of the tube at the centre is about 70 feet. At the end of the tubes bed-plates and rollers allow of their free extension and contraction under varying temperatures. The whole is constructed of malleable iron plates, strongly rivetted together. The total quantity of wrought iron in the bridge is 2,650 tons, of cast iron about 1,200 tons, and of masonry and brickwork for the piers about 17,000 cubic yards, and of timber about 14,000 cubic feet. Total cost, £230,000.

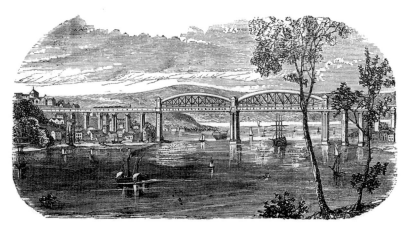

Royal Albert Bridge.

FLOATING THE FIRST TUBE

OF THE

ROYAL ALBERT BRIDGE,

SEPTEMBER 1st, 1857.

Cornwall was practically a region "beyond railways." With the exception of the short West Cornwall line running from Truro to Penzance, the means of locomotion was restricted to a few interesting relics of the stage-coach era of England, and the venerable auxiliaries of cars and vans reinforced by the more modern achievement of omnibuses. The project of a railway through Cornwall, to unite the western county in iron fellowship with the rest of England, has had its discouraging and costly history. In 1844 the Cornwall Railway Company was formed, and in the excess of speculation, if not in exuberance of capital, a rival scheme soon started upon the stage. The struggle was obstinate and expensive, and the result was the rejection by Parliament of both sets of plans. Eventually, after an expenditure by [the] Cornwall Company of no less a sum than £100,000, it succeeded in passing its bill through both Houses, and on the 3rd of August 1846, it received the Royal Assent.

Mr. Brunel was the engineer of the new line, which was to run down by St. Germans' River, skirting the shore until it reached Saltash, and then to cross by a bridge to the opposite shore, and thus to reach the joint station at Plymouth. It was about this time that Mr. Stephenson completed his design for the Britannia Bridge at the Menai Straits, and at the expense, it is said, of about £600,000, executed the tubular bridge which has been so generally applauded. In 1848, the late Mr. William Glennie the local engineer of the Cornwall line, under Mr. Brunel's direction, prepared an iron tube [of] 6 feet diameter, to effect a practical boring of the mud and clay at the bottom of the river, to ascertain what depth would be needful to reach the rock, and the possibility of building a centre pier by means of an iron cylinder, instead of the expensive mode of a pile coffer dam. The experiments were eminently successful, but, owing to the impossibility of raising the necessary capital, the works on the line were suspended from the beginning of 1849 to 1852, when Mr. Brunel proceeded with his plans and by the end of 1853 completed them. The Saltash Bridge presented difficulties which did not exist in the case of the Menai Bridge. In the centre of the Menai Straits, nature had placed a rock rising above the surface of the water, but no such help was afforded in the Tamar – a depth of 85 feet below high-water mark had to be sounded, and a space of 36 feet in diameter clay and mud, to be excavated, and the rock to be levelled into steps to place an artificial rock of sufficient magnitude and strength to receive the superstructure of 2,000 or 3,000 tons of iron. But the natural difficulties attending this undertaking never shook the confidence of the engineer, or diminished the energy with which the work was prosecuted. A very beautiful and appropriate "plant" was soon brought to the east side of the Tamar, and operations were then busily commenced. A water-tight tube, 36 feet in diameter and 95 feet long, constructed with air-tight chambers, and a cupola, about one-third from the bottom, was made ready for floating, and, to the surprise of the uninitiated, it was easily floated off from the work-shops, and, by the simplest contrivance, was sunk perpendicularly in the very spot, in the centre of the Tamar, where Mr. Brunel intended. This being done, the excavations for the purpose of securing the foundations for the central pier were commenced. The bed of the river was speedily removed but an unexpected difficulty presented itself from there being a fissure in the rock immediately under the cylinder, and it was necessary to stop this before any of the masonry could be carried on. This effected, the pier gradually rose, and to the gratification of those who had watched the proceedings with much interest, a strong granite column appeared above the tide, and it was soon announced that the first part of the undertaking was complete. In the meantime the tube and roadway progressed, combining the tubular and chain suspension principles, and instead of a massive structure like the Britannia, affording an iron tunnel for the trains, the roadway is suspended from the tubes, the whole forming a light, elegant and substantial structure at much less cost, and equal, if not superior, in efficiency secured.

It was on Tuesday, the first of September, 1857, that steps were taken for raising and floating off the first tube from the yard where it was built, and landing it on the piers. The day was beautifully fine, and an immense number of people assembled to witness the undertaking.

No vessel or boat was allowed to approach the piers, but below the notice which announced this regulation, the river was alive with yachts containing gaily dressed pleasure parties. There were also innumerable boats in all directions. Within the town of Saltash the utmost gaiety prevailed. Flags were suspended from houses, the church bells rang merry peals, and the inhabitants evinced great anxiety to do honour to the event.

The arrangements were of the most complete description. Temporary docks were cut at the ends of the tube for the admission of four pontoons – two at each end. The pontoons drew about 8 ft. 6 in. of water, and were capable of sustaining a weight of 500 tons each, or 2,000 tons in the whole. As the weight of the section which they had to float is 1,100 tons it will be seen that ample power had been provided. By means of valves the pontoons admit water into their interiors, and having by this means been sunk to some extent, they were passed beneath the ends of the tubes. Five vessels, borrowed from the Government authorities, were moored in different positions in the river, one being placed on the eastern side, another in the centre of the stream and a third at the western side, above the bridge; and the other two being moored lower down. On board these were stationed a number of men from the dockyard and her Majesty's ships, with powerful crabs for the purpose of warping the tube to its position. Four more hawsers were attached to as many windlasses at different points on shore and arrangements had been made to guide and control the pontoons in every direction as they floated onwards with their gigantic burden.

The plan adopted for directing the operations of the workmen and labourers engaged, was that of signal flags from a temporary platform, in the centre of the tube, which was under the immediate and entire control of Mr. Brunel. Early in the morning, the men were engaged in pumping out the water which had been let into the pontoons, in order to render them more buoyant, and as the tide rose they rose also, and thus the ponderous weight of the tube was thrown upon them. It was calculated that the tide would rise sufficiently to float the mass soon after 1 o'clock, and at 1h. 15m. the monster tube was seen to float. Gradually it moved out, first one end and then the other, until it reached the centre. The assembled crowds saw with astonishment this huge mass moving without the slightest sound. Not a voice was heard, not a direction was spoken; a few flags waved, a few boards with numbers on them were exhibited, and, as by some mysterious agency, the tube and rail borne on the pontoons travelled to their resting-place, and with such quietude as marked the building of Solomon's temple. With the impressive silence which is the highest evidence of power, it *slid*, as it were into its position without an accident, without any extraordinary mechanical effort, without a "misfit" to the extent of the eighth of an inch. Equally without haste and without delay, just as the tide reached its limit, at 3 o'clock, the tube was fixed on the piers 30 feet above high-water, and the band of the Royal Marines, which was stationed in a vessel near Saltash, struck up "See the conquering hero comes," and then "God save the Queen," when the assembled multitude broke out into loud and continued cheers in expression of their admiration and delight. Numbers of boats immediately passed under the railway, which was some eight feet above high-water, and people touched the iron rod ere it should become elevated to the height it was destined to occupy. The tube presented a very singular appearance, and will form a most striking permanent addition to the "attractions of the Tamar." The only bridge of a similar construction in the country is that at Chepstow, also planned by Mr. Brunel.

At five o'clock the tide was found to have sufficiently receded for the removal of the pontoons. The shores were knocked away, the wedges were removed, and the heavy mass raised independently on the piers from which it has been gradually raised by hydraulic pressure. For this purpose the hydraulic presses were fixed, and the first *lift* of the tube was made on the 25th November, 1857, and raised to its final lofty position [on] May 19th, 1858.

As might have been anticipated, the event excited the utmost interest not only in the Three Towns, but throughout both counties. In addition to the important influence which the completion of the bridge must have on the commercial prosperity of the two counties, the undertaking, in an engineering point of view, was well calculated to excite the interest of all who are in any way connected with that department. As, therefore, few persons of the present generation, even should they attain the fabulous age of that wonderful person who is described as the "oldest inhabitant", were ever likely again to witness the completion of such another feat of engineering skill, persons of all grades determined to enjoy the sight. Accordingly throughout the previous day there were evident indications that in the Three Towns the event was intended to be celebrated as a general holiday. Every cab was engaged to take parties to Saltash, the fare being advanced from 5s. to 20s., and even at that high rate of charge the supply fell short of the demand. The Saltash Steam Packet Companies brought all their steamers into operation, and borrowed more, but though they ran up and down every half-hour, they could not accommodate all applicants, notwithstanding the vessels were at times crammed with living freights, to an extent that caused them to roll about and dip in a manner that was truly alarming. From an early hour in the morning, crowds of visitors continued to pour into Saltash from all quarters; but towards one o'clock, when the public establishment and other workshops had suspended work, the arrivals were immense. But the visitors comprised numerous parties besides the resident[s] of this neighbourhood; Calstock, St. Germans, Truro, and the intermediate towns, Exeter, and even London, sent their thousands to swell the immense throng. Never did Saltash present such an appearance before. Not only was every spot within the town which commanded a view of the bridge, packed as closely as it was possible for the people to stand, but the elevated grounds above it were covered. The shore on the opposite side, far up the Saltash road, was closely packed and the fields adjoining, fronting Saltash, also contained their thousands. A shilling for standing-room in a tolerable position was not considered an extravagant price, and we have heard of one enterprising individual who paid as much as £30 for the occupation of a field during the day, and who reimbursed himself by imposing a certain charge on visitors entering it.

The people of Saltash were not behind hand either in their desire duly to do honour to the event, or to provide for the immense concourse which it was evident would visit them. Flags were suspended across several of the streets; the church bells pealed forth their cheerful notes of welcome from an early hour; tents and marquees were erected in private gardens for the accommodation of friends, while for the accommodation of strangers, the various houses of entertainment had laid in enormous stores of edibles and drinkables. The provision, however, fell short of the demand, and we heard that before the evening closed, Saltash was regularly cleared out, there being scarcely anything edible left in the whole town. To estimate the numbers that were present is impossible, but at a low computation we should say that it amounted at least to from 30,000 to 40,000.

To Mr. Brunel, the engineer, whose genius had been exercised in designing, constructing, and planning this enormous mass of iron, and to Captain Claxton, R.N., whose aid in placing and directing the various detachments of seamen and labourers by whom all this was accomplished, is this great feat of engineering skill and mechanical contrivance entirely owing.

We ought to state that M. Williams, Esq., M.P., the Chairman of the Cornwall Railway Company, was on the bridge with Mr. Brunel from the commencement to the termination of the ceremony, being the only gentlemen not professionally engaged, who was present at the time.

In a room adjoining the western pier, an excellent *dejeuner* was provided by Mr. Holmes, of George-street, Plymouth, to which the directors, and their friends, and the officials of the company, sat down during the afternoon. Several toasts were drunk with the utmost enthusiasm, among which were "Prosperity to the Cornwall Railway Company," "the Health of Mr. Brunel, the engineer of the line," and the "Albert Bridge," and "the Health of the Mayor of Saltash."

It is gratifying to add that, notwithstanding the large numbers of private and public carriages that were at the passage during the day, and the immense

Floating the first Tube of the Royal Albert Bridge.

number of persons on both sides of the water, large bodies of whom were constantly crossing and re-crossing, not the slightest accident occurred throughout.

We may mention that Mr. Brereton, Mr. Brunel's head draughtsman was actively engaged, as were also Mr. Gainsford the local superintendent of works, and Mr. Wakefield, assistant to Mr. Gainsford. Amongst those who witnessed the undertaking, were – The Earl and Countess of Morley, Lord Stanley, the Marquis of Salisbury, W. Davey, Esq., M.P., T. J. A. Robartes, Esq., M.P., J. W. Buller, Esq., M.P., E. Divett, Esq., M.P., and many of the directors of the Cornwall Railway, and the associated companies; as also the Dockyard and other authorities, both naval and military.

FLOATING THE SECOND TUBE

OF THE

ROYAL ALBERT BRIDGE,

JULY 10th, 1858.

The last difficulty in the construction of the Cornwall Railway is now surmounted. Henceforth old Tamar will be spanned by its double ferruginous bow, presenting with Cyclopean triumph a grand highway of commerce across the broad bosom of the waters. It disputes no territory with the waves; it raises its own dominion over them. The restless ebb and flow are undisturbed, every inch of bank and bed owned by the grand Hamoaze remains true to its ancient natural fealty. The river has its own rights, and its own powers – which might be over-reached, but never overcome – are imperial, everlasting. But whilst nature on her separate moods and aspects speak to man of absolute diversity and unequal conflict, in her abstract teaching she has no hint of baffled work, but rather offer to him the material for illimitable victories. Thus we have the way of making crooked places straight, and rough places plain, by the splendid system of *ironing* the earth; thus we leave the waters their mighty forces and indisputable control, but we stretch over them with iron arms, and join the divisions and connect the distances they create. Iron is everywhere; in the earth, and in the blood, and in the brain. It is the foundation of art, skill, and science. It compensates for sinews, it is the name for strength, it laughs at obstacles, it gives to greatness a new standard, it works miracles – and, as the servant of human genius and toil, it allows man to become a mightier master day by day.

Saturday, the 10th of July, was the day fixed for floating the second and last tube of the Royal Albert (Iron) Bridge, and we have the satisfaction to state that the work was accomplished in the most successful manner. In the absence of Mr. Brunel, the operation was conducted under the direction of Mr. Gainsford, and other gentlemen of Mr. Brunel's staff. The course adopted was precisely similar to that observed in the floating of the first tube, which was superintended by Mr. Brunel. The first plate of the second tube was laid on the 20th November, 1857, and it was completed and lifted on the pontoons ready for floating on the 30th of June, 1858, the very day on which the time of the contract expired. The rapidity and precision with which the work was advanced was highly creditable to Messrs. Hudson and Male, the contractors under the Cornwall Railway Company, for building the tube. It is of similar dimensions and construction to the first, nothing having been discovered as a fault in the first tube, which it was found necessary to correct in the second. Like the first this tube is composed of plates of thick sheet iron riveted together. Its shape on the end is oval 17 feet wide by 12 deep. It is 455 feet long, forming the segment of a circle, and having a rise of 28 feet, and with the roadway and suspension rods, which were all in place before the tube was floated, it weighed about 1,100 tons. The operation of floating was thus conducted. Under each end, sufficiently far in to be clear of the bearing surface, supporters formed of balks of timber were erected, the end of these supporters being fixed to pontoons, two of which were placed at each end of the tube. These supporters formed a complete forest, and were the subject of enquiry by a few of the uninitiated who, thinking this wood-work was part of the bridge, suggested that it was mis-named an iron bridge. Water had been admitted into the pontoons during the time the tube and its appendages had been erecting, but on the day of what was termed the "launching" it, the water was shut out sufficiently to float the pontoons and the ponderous weight they bore on the rising of the tide. At about two o'clock the tube was announced to be afloat, and shortly after it was gradually seen to move away from the stage where it had been built. This was done by means of warps, which were judiciously led from five vessels moored firmly in position at convenient distances from the floating mass. On board these vessels was a number of blue-jackets from the *Exmouth,* kindly lent by the Port Admiral for the occasion, and under the command of Commander Risk, who fulfilled a similar important duty on the occasion of the floating of the first tube. The orders were given noiselessly by means of signals (consisting of numbers and flags). After being afloat the tube was warped a short way up the harbour to clear the eastern pier, and then brought round to its place with the greatest possible precision, notwithstanding a very strong wind was blowing from the north-east, which must have rendered the work considerably more difficult in being accomplished. The two ends of the tube were fixed on the piers built to receive them at about a quarter after five o'clock; the gratifying intelligence that the work was successfully performed being announced by the hearty cheers of the workmen, which were taken up by the spectators from every vessel on the water and along the shores of the river. The pontoons were removed in the evening, and the tube left to rest on the piers, which was raised to about 100 feet, the tube being lifted by hydraulic power whilst the work was being done. We should not omit to state that Mr. Whitting had the direction of the working parties afloat, where his great skill and practical knowledge were of the highest value. Mr. Brereton, superintending engineer of works being carried out by Mr. Brunel in London, was present on the occasion. Mr. Thompson Her Majesty's Harbour Master, was at the "scene of action," and rendered efficient service, as did also Captain Claxton.

The directors of the Cornwall Railway issued a large number of tickets for persons to view the floating from the yard, where a capital view of the whole arrangements was obtained. Here an excellent luncheon was provided by Mr. Holmes, of George Street, Plymouth, which proved very acceptable to the visitors. Among those present were the chairman, directors, and staffs of the South Devon, Cornwall, and Bristol and Exeter Railways; Captain Harrison, of the *Great Eastern* steamship; the Mayor of Saltash, etc., etc.

Admiral Sir Barrington Reynolds, Rear-Admiral Superintendent, Sir Thomas Pasley, and Major-General Eden, were amongst those who witnessed the gratifying proceedings afloat.

On the completion of the work for the day, a telegram was immediately sent by Mr. Brereton to Mr. Brunel at Lausanne, that the floating of the tube had been attended with complete success. The first lift of the second tube was made on the 9th August, and was gradually raised by hydraulic pressure like the first tube; and this wonderful structure was formally opened by the late lamented Prince Consort, amidst much public rejoicing and festivity on the 2nd of May, 1859. – The traffic on the line begun on the following day.

An early print dating back to around the 1860s, showing the bridge from the Cornwall side and the general view looking up the River Tamar.

Author's collection

14

September, 1859.

CORNWALL RAILWAY.

Miles	STATIONS.	Week Days. Class 1, 2, 3	Ex. 1 & 2	Class 1 & 2	Mail 1 & 2	Class 1, 2, 3	Sundays. Class 1, 2, 3	Mail 1, 2, 3	Class 1, 2, 3
		a.m.	a.m.	a.m.	p.m.	p.m.	a.m.	p.m.	p.m.
—	Truro . . . . dep.	5 45	8 20	11 0	3 55	6 55	6 50	3 55	. .
7¼	Grampound Road . . arr.	6 3	. .	11 18	4 13	7 13	7 8	4 13	. .
14¼	St. Austell	6 18	8 50	11 35	4 30	7 30	7 25	4 30	. .
18¾	Par	6 30	. .	11 50	4 42	7 42	7 37	4 42	. .
23¼	Lostwithiel	6 42	9 10	12 5	4 55	7 55	7 50	4 55	. .
26	Bodmin Road	6 50	9 20	12 15	5 5	8 5	8 0	5 5	. .
35¾	Liskeard	7 15	9 40	12 40	5 30	8 30	8 25	5 30	8 30
38¾	Menheniot	7 30	. .	12 55	5 40	8 45	8 35	5 40	8 45
44¼	St. Germans	7 45	. .	1 10	5 55	9 0	8 50	5 55	9 0
49¼	Saltash	8 5	10 15	1 30	6 15	9 15	9 15	6 15	9 25
52¼	Devonport	8 20	. .	1 40	6 30	9 25	9 25	6 30	9 35
53¾	Plymouth	8 30	10 30	1 50	6 40	9 35	9 35	6 40	9 45
	Plymouth, S.D.R. . . . . . dep.	8 55	10 45	2 10	7 10	. .	12 0	7 10	. .
	Exeter . . . . arr.	11 35	12 45	5 10	9 35	. .	2 30	9 35	. .
	Bristol, B. & E.R.	3 45	2 45	8 50	12 25	. .	5 20	12 25	. .
	Paddington, G.W.R.	9 15	6 0	. .	4 45	. .	10 20	. .	. .

Miles	STATIONS.	Week Days.					Sundays.		
		p.m.	a.m.	p.m.	a.m.	a.m.	a.m.	a.m.	
	Paddington, G.W.R. . . dep.	8 10	. .	. .	9 30	6 0	. .	. .	. .
	Bristol, B. & E.R.	12 40	. .	7 50	12 50	11 30	12 40	7 50	. .
	Exeter, S D.R.	3 30	6 45	10 50	3 0	4 20	3 30	10 50	. .
	Plymouth, S.D.R. . . . . . arr.	5 45	9 35	1 25	5 5	7 5	5 45	1 25	. .
		Mail 1, 2, 3	Class 1 & 2	Class 1, 2, 3	Ex. 1 & 2	Class 1 & 2	Mail 1, 2, 3	1, 2, 3	Class 1, 2, 3
		a.m.	a.m.	p.m.	p.m.	p.m.	a.m.	p.m.	p.m.
—	Plymouth . . . . . dep.	6 5	10 0	2 20	5 25	7 30	6 5	2 20	4 5
1½	Devonport . . . . . arr.	6 10	10 5	2 30	. .	7 35	6 10	2 30	4 10
4¼	Saltash	6 20	10 15	2 40	5 35	7 45	6 20	2 40	4 20
9½	St. Germans	6 40	10 30	2 55	. .	8 0	6 40	2 55	4 45
14¾	Menheniot	6 55	10 45	3 10	. .	8 15	6 55	3 10	5 0
18	Liskeard	7 15	11 0	3 25	6 5	8 30	7 15	3 25	5 10
27¾	Bodmin Road	7 40	11 25	3 50	6 30	8 55	7 40	3 50	
30½	Lostwithiel	7 50	11 35	4 0	6 38	9 5	7 50	4 0	. .
34¾	Par	8 3	11 50	4 15	. .	9 20	8 3	4 15	. .
39¼	St. Austell	8 15	12 5	4 30	7 3	9 35	8 15	4 30	. .
46¼	Grampound Road . .	8 30	12 20	4 45	. .	9 55	8 30	4 45	. .
53¾	Truro	8 55	12 40	5 5	7 30	10 20	8 55	5 5	. .

Greenwich Time is kept at all Stations. It is 20 minutes earlier than Truro, and 17 minutes earlier than Devonport and Plymouth time.

Omnibuses leave Truro for Falmouth and Penryn from every Train except to the first and from the last. Flys always in attendance. The West Cornwall Railway takes on Passengers and Parcels to Redruth, Camborne, Hayle, and Penzance.

The timetable issued by the Cornwall Railway Company shortly after the opening of the Royal Albert Bridge on 2nd May 1859.

Bryan Gibson collection

POSTSCRIPT

'The Saltash Bridge is unique in design and form of construction. It combines three classical engineering forms – the compression arch, the tension chain and the beam deck. But it is a rare type, using what is called a "closed system", i.e. the forces are all contained within the structure. Certainly in terms of railway bridges, Saltash is unique – and very clever.'

These are the words of the engineer Anthony Hunt included in an article appearing in the *Western Morning News* on 18th November 2000. Coming more than 140 years after the single-track bridge was constructed, they could, perhaps, be regarded as the ultimate compliment to Brunel, whose task had been compounded not only by problems in finding a footing for the central pier some 85 feet below high water level, but also by the Admiralty specifying that the bridge's deck height should be 100 feet above high water level.

Despite such a long passage of time, it is also a tribute to Brunel that the bridge has remained substantially unaltered over the years, certainly as regards its general appearance. Even then, most of the 'improvements' carried out have been done merely to strengthen the bridge in order for it to be able to cope with engines and rolling stock, in particular, far heavier than Brunel could ever have envisaged. Brief details of these alterations and other important facts, together with dates, are included below in order to complete this short account of Brunel's magnificent achievement in spanning the River Tamar between St Budeaux (Plymouth) and Saltash.

Some important dates during the history of the bridge.

1859
(2nd May)
– The ceremonious opening of the bridge by Prince Albert took place. Brunel, by now a sick and dying man, was unable to attend. He did, however, view his masterpiece later that month by being drawn across it on a couch in an open truck; sadly, he died in the following September.

1905
– The installation of 401 additional new cross-girders was carried out, so strengthening the timber decking on which the track lay.

At around this time plans were also made to replace the first two approach spans on the Cornwall side in order to allow the double line and platforms at Saltash Station to be extended, this latter task being completed in 1908.

1928
– Work on replacing the remaining fifteen approach spans (eight on the Cornwall side and seven on the Devon side) commenced

following a report made to the Great Western Board in July 1927 which stated that the original wrought iron girders of 1859 were no longer of full strength and that their renewal was necessary at an early date. A special 18¹/₂-ton vehicle had to be constructed for the purpose as cranes could not be used 'on the skew'. (Trains were kept running during the work, but were delayed!)

1939/46 – The bridge remained intact despite the heavy bombing of Plymouth (particularly during the Blitz of March and April 1941) and notwithstanding its close proximity to the dockyard and other military installations. (One assumes that Hitler required the connection between Devon and Cornwall to be maintained for military use after he had conquered Britain!) However, heavy and excessive wartime usage did take its toll and not surprisingly, with no or little routine maintenance work carried out, there were breakages. To overcome these, temporary remedial measures were taken to keep the bridge in service, which took the form of enveloping the chains with heavy strapping.

During 1940 sleepers were laid between the track on the bridge to enable military vehicles to cross it as and when the need arose or in the event of the ferries becoming disabled. On these occasions trains had to be stopped, a token taken out and a GWR pilotman would have to ride on the last vehicle across the bridge, which was generally a Bren gun carrier. At the Saltash end, in order to cope with this somewhat unusual traffic, the automatic train control ramp had to be removed from the bridge approach and placed in a new position by the goods shed, and the signalling altered accordingly; this remained in effect until 1st September 1946, when normal, peacetime railway working resumed.

1958/9 – With the centenary in mind, British Railways gave the bridge a full repaint, it being finished in a dull silver colour.

For the summer of 1959 only, the ladders and walkways which normally partially obscure the lettering 'I.K. BRUNEL – ENGINEER – 1859' above the entrance archways at either end were removed and the bridge was floodlit each night.

1960 – The temporary repairs executed during wartime were finally made permanent by completely altering the connections with

17

A selection of tickets issued for the centenary, including two for journeys *not* involving the crossing of the bridge.

the ironwork. In this action, some wrought iron was replaced by mild steel, which was fastened to the remainder of the original work by means of high-tensile steel bolts and incorporated lubrication and phosphor-bronze liners to cater for any movement within the structure and to combat the ingress of water. At the same time other modifications were also carried out in order to 'stiffen' the bridge so that it could cope with the ever-increasing weight of trains crossing it.

1961   –   From June of this year, following the opening of the Associated Portland Cement Works at Chelson Meadow, Plymouth, trains of 20-ton 'Prestflo' bulk cement wagons heading for the storage and distribution silos at Chasewater in Cornwall added still further to the amount of loading on the bridge.

1967/8   –   From February 1967 heavy china clay trains started travelling from Burngullow in Cornwall to Sittingbourne in Kent, and these were said to be imposing axle-loadings of $22^1/_2$ tons on the bridge. However, the final straw came during the following year, when trains of 100-ton bogie wagons, transporting china clay waste out of Cornwall for use as a building material, started crossing the bridge; this necessitated the bracing of the chains to the plate girders of the track deck by means of large steel diagonals, as can clearly be seen in John Gilpin's photograph appearing on the back cover of this book.

2006   –   After almost 150 years, and after only relatively modest maintenance costs, the Royal Albert Bridge continues to play a vital role in linking Cornwall to Devon by rail. In so doing, it has proved more than capable of meeting the demands of today's modern fleet of trains, which, in itself, only serves to highlight yet again the ingenuity of its creator – the great Isambard Kingdom Brunel, whose birth on 9th April 1806 is about to be celebrated nationwide.

❋ ❋ ❋ ❋ ❋

THE ROYAL ALBERT BRIDGE

A pictorial survey

A broad-gauge train heads out of Saltash Station and onto the bridge in the late 1880s.

Author's collection

A view up the River Tamar from Wearde Quay on the Cornwall side. Painting or maintenance must be in progress, as under-slung scaffolding can be seen at the second pier on the left-hand side of the picture (c.1892).

J. B. N. Ashford

Three studies of the spans and track bed of the bridge shortly after the transfer from broad to standard gauge in May 1892. They were taken on the Plymouth side, looking towards Saltash, when the bridge was just over 30 years old.

It will be observed that the track appears to be off centre, and to the left, but this is an optical illusion. This impression is gained from the fact that a wooden 'cess', or walkway, is situated to the left of the track, covering much of the clean ballast, whilst to the right of the track all the clean ballast is on view.

It is quite possible that, immediately following conversion, the track was left of centre. This was a product of the engineering of the conversion itself, for the quickest way to convert 7 feet $0^{1}/_{4}$ inch to 4 feet $8^{1}/_{2}$ inches was to shift the outer rail closer by 2 feet $3^{3}/_{4}$ inches. This allowed access to station platforms to be maintained, and for adjustments to positioning to be executed when normal track replacement and repairs took place later.

Finally, other points of interest are the wooden casing carrying telegraph cables affixed above the 'cess' on the left-hand side, and the signal wires slung on pulleys on the right-hand side.

J. B. N. Ashford

Two Dean 4–4–0s double head a fine rake of eleven clerestory coaches, seen here leaving the Devon side of the bridge. It will be noted that the Saltash 'down distant' signal appears to be red as per the 'home' signal above it. This, and other 'distant' signals, did not change to yellow until 1930 when GWR policy itself changed, commencing at Paddington and working westwards to the rest of the system (c.1900).

J. B. N. Ashford

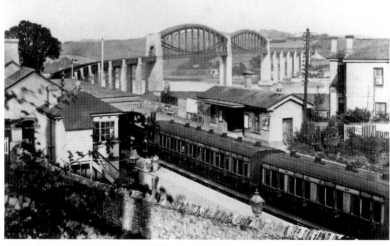

A local train, headed by a '507' class 2–4–0T, waits for the 'off' at Saltash with a stopper to Plymouth (c.1904/5).

Author's collection

A steam railcar and its trailer enter the first arch after leaving the Devon side (c.1905).

Author's collection

A typical postcard of the time showing the bridge with a train crossing it (c.1916).

Author's collection

For that time, a rare view taken from the air of the Royal Albert Bridge. The steam-operated car ferry bridge is in centre stream. Also, the Southern Railway main line to Waterloo is seen towards the top right-hand side of the picture (c.1930).

Chapman & Son

The ROYAL ALBERT BRIDGE, SALTASH
Brunel's famous link between Glorious Devon and The Cornish Riviera

A typical GWR travel poster of the 1930s showing the bridge.
Reproduced courtesy of British Railways Board

The penultimate year before nationalisation sees a GWR 0–6–0PT and two autocoaches heading for the next stop, St Budeaux Station (c.1946).

Chapman & Son

No. 7031 *Cromwells Castle* leaves the eastern end of the bridge with an 'up' express during the late 1950s.

Chapman & Son

A view of the Coombe-by-Saltash viaduct, with the River Tamar and the Royal Albert Bridge in the background. The train which can just be seen crossing the bridge is the second part of the Cornish Riviera Express on 25th July 1959 and is being hauled by ex-GWR 4–6–0s Nos. 7816 *Frilsham Manor* and 1021 *County of Montgomery.*

Peter W. Gray

The bridge floodlit for the centenary celebrations (August 1959).

John Gilpin

The 'Royal Duchy', behind 4–6–0 No. 6832 *Brockton Grange,* proceeds across the bridge from Saltash on 29th September 1959.

Peter W. Gray

A local train from Saltash to Plymouth, with 0–6–0PT No. 6400 in charge (c.1960).

Chapman & Son

A 'Warship' class diesel locomotive leaves the eastern end of the bridge with an 'up' passenger train, whilst the 'road competition' draws ever nearer in the background! (c.1960).

Chapman & Son

No. 34002 *Salisbury* awaits the 'off' from platform 5 at Plymouth (North Road) with a joint RCTS/PRC special to Penzance on 3rd May 1964. At the time, this locomotive was just minutes away from being the first ex-Southern Railway 'West Country' class 4–6–2 to cross the Royal Albert Bridge.

Author

A class 50 diesel returns from Cornwall with a superb rake of Great Western coaching stock used for a special tour, namely 'The Severn Valley Railway Limited' (c.1977).

Author

A study of the bridge offering a direct comparison with the lower photograph appearing on page 21. This was taken when the Plymouth Railway Circle took part in a conducted tour of the bridge on 6th June 1990.

John Gilpin

An unusual view of the inside of one of the tubes of the bridge. This was another study taken during the Plymouth Railway Circle's conducted tour of the bridge on 6th June 1990.

John Gilpin

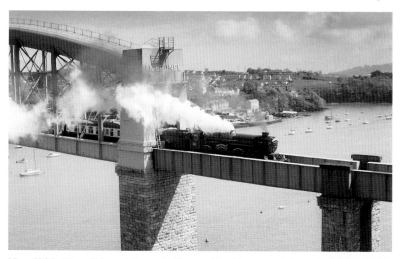

No. 6024 *King Edward I* enters Cornwall with a special on 2nd May 1998. Unlike many years earlier, before the bridge was strengthened, a 'double red' classification locomotive (i.e. a 'King') or two 'single red' locomotives coupled together (such as a 'Castle' and a 'Hall') are now allowed to cross it.

John Gilpin

An unusual view of the bridge glimpsed between the legs of one of its approach spans, 19th February 2000.

John Gilpin

An artistic study of the two bridges now crossing the Tamar, shown against a clear blue April sky and taken from the old Saltash ferry slipway, 16th April 2002.

John Gilpin

BIBLIOGRAPHY

There have been so many books published that include reference to the Royal Albert Bridge that I have restricted the entries in this Bibliography to just three that I have found particularly useful as sources of reference.

History of the Great Western Railway Volume Two (1863–1921), E. T. MacDermot – revised by C. R. Clinker (Ian Allan, 1964)

The Girder Bridge, after Brunel and others, P. S. A. Berridge, MBE, FICE (Wheatons Ltd, 1969)

Track Topics, W. G. Chapman (Great Western Railway, 1935 – reprinted by Patrick Stephens Ltd, 1971)

✳ ✳ ✳ ✳ ✳

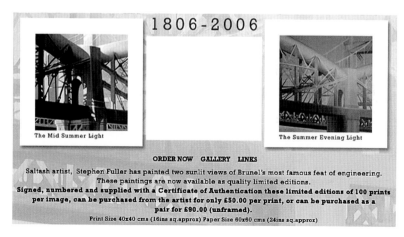